SIX STEPS TO LOVING YOUR CHURCH

COLIN MARSHALL
AND TONY PAYNE

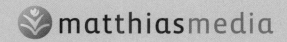

Matthias Media
(St Matthias Press Ltd ACN 067 558 365)
Email: info@matthiasmedia.com.au
Internet: www.matthiasmedia.com.au
Please visit our website for current postal and telephone contact information.

Matthias Media (USA)
Email: sales@matthiasmedia.com
Internet: www.matthiasmedia.com
Please visit our website for current postal and telephone contact information.

ISBN 978 1 922206 43 5

Cover design and typesetting by Lankshear Design.

CONTENTS

INTRODUCTION

Some of us really love our churches, some of us aren't so positive, and for many of us that feeling can change from week to week.

This six-session program is about how to love your church whether you're feeling enthusiastic about it or not. It's about the mindset we take with us as we go to church each week, and how that mindset is expressed in a multitude of ways, big and small. In particular, it's about the part that we all play as God's people in loving, serving and building each other up, Sunday by Sunday. We all have a ministry—the ministry of the pew.[1]

Over the six sessions of the course we will cover subjects such as:

- our current attitudes towards church, and how they are expressed
- what the Bible says about the meaning and purpose of church
- what it means to love our church and the people who go there
- how we can be active encouraging servants before, during and after church, rather than just consumers or spectators.

Each session contains a mix of discussion, Bible study, video input and prayer, along with simple exercises to help you put the ideas into practice on Sunday.

Our prayer is that the fairly simple and practical ideas in this training program will change the way you think and act at church, and bear fruit in the lives of those around for years to come.

Colin Marshall and Tony Payne
August 2013

---

1. This phrase goes back to a widely read article that Colin wrote in 1994 for *The Briefing*. You can read it here: matthiasmedia.com.au/briefing/library/1855

WALKING INTO CHURCH

Getting started

 **Video: How do you walk into church?**

Notes on video

⊖ Discuss: Your church

1. What sort of things do you normally think about as you walk into church?

2. What do you really love about church at the moment?

3. What do you find hard (if anything) about church at the moment?

4. When the New Testament Christians walked into church, they weren't walking into a purpose-built religious-looking building. Mostly they were walking into someone's home. How do you think this would have affected the way they thought about walking into church?

5. What do you think *God* is thinking about as you walk into church?

6. Read Ephesians 5:25-27 and 1 Corinthians 3:10-17. What do these passages teach about God's attitude towards the church?

 **Video: What is God thinking?**

Notes on video

⏩ Discuss: A different walk

1. What struck you most from the video about God and the church?

2. What difference would it make, do you think, if you were to pray as you walked into church?

3. Think about the people at your church:

   - Who is new in the past 12 months? Do you know why they came to your church?

   - What do new people tend to do at the end of your church service?

   - Have any of the regulars been absent recently? Do you know why?

4. Think about your own habits at church:

- Where do you normally sit? Why there?

- Who do you normally speak with?

- What do you tend to do after the meeting finishes?

 **Prayer**

Close the session with a brief time of prayer, giving thanks for your church and for God's great love for us.

Assignment

This coming Sunday, don't sit in your 'normal' seat (if you have one). Pray about where to sit, and sit next to someone different.

BUILDING IN LOVE

 **Discuss**

Did you remember to pray and to sit somewhere different? How did it go?

 **Video: Building or spectating?**

Notes on video

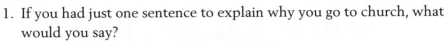

Bible study: Building in love

1. If you had just one sentence to explain why you go to church, what would you say?

Read 1 Corinthians 13:1-7.
2. The famous chapter on love is part of Paul's teaching on using one's gifts in church. Why do you think he describes love as the "more excellent way" (1 Cor 12:31)?

3. Look at the different ways in which love is described in verses 4-7. How would these attitudes apply to our behaviour in church?

Read 1 Corinthians 14:1-12, 26-33.
4. What is it about prophecy that makes it better than speaking in tongues in church?

5. How do you think this relates to love in chapter 13?

6. What guidelines are given as to who should speak in the gathering, and how?

Now read Hebrews 10:19-25.
7. How do we gain access to God, according to this passage (vv. 19-22)?

8. Why then do we gather together (vv. 23-25)?

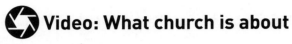 Video: What church is about

Notes on video

🅑 Discuss: Are you a builder?

1. Look back at your one-sentence summary of why you go to church (question 1 on page 14). How would you change your sentence in light of what we've seen from the Bible?

2. What might be the symptoms of a consumer or spectator attitude to church?

3. What might be the fruits of a servant attitude to church?

4. Do you think it might be possible to 'love' your church without actually 'loving' your church? How?

5. Optional: if you have time, look up one or more of the following passages. What motivates us to serve one another at church and beyond?

- Mark 10:41-45

- John 13:12-17

- 1 Corinthians 10:31-11:1

- Ephesians 5:1-2

- Philippians 2:1-11

Prayer

- Give thanks for God's great gift of fellowship—that we have been saved into a family, with brothers and sisters for mutual help and encouragement.
- Pray for your attitude towards church. Pray that God would give you a loving, other-person-centred heart.

Assignment

This Sunday, in the first few minutes after the service, look for a way to practically serve another person (e.g. get a coffee for someone, take a new person to the welcome table, help with packing up, and so on).

Have a conversation with someone after church. Ask them how their week has been, and ask what you could pray for them.

GET READY TO BUILD

 **Discuss**

1. How did you go in finding a practical way to serve or help someone after the service?

2. Did you manage to ask someone in conversation what you could pray for them? What effect did it have on the conversation?

 **Video: Preparing to build**

Notes on video

 **Discuss: Be prepared**

If your goal is to build and encourage people at church, what could you do beforehand to prepare? See how many ideas you can come up with.

 # Video: How to build during the meeting

Notes on video

 ## Discuss: Better building

1. What's your facial 'screen saver' during the sermon?

2. What other practical ideas can you come up with for being a better builder during church?

3. What one or two things could you work on to be more of a 'builder' during the church meeting?

 Prayer

- Pray for one another, that God would help you to put love into action this Sunday.
- Pray for the people you spoke with last Sunday (and for any of their prayer points).

 Assignment

1. Choose at least one new thing you could do *before* church to prepare to build, and put it into practice this week.

2. Choose at least one new thing you could do *during* church to encourage and help others, and put it into practice this Sunday.

LOVE OVER COFFEE

 Discuss

1. Report back on your efforts to prepare to build *before* church. What did you try?

2. How did you go being an active builder *during* church?

 Video: When does church finish?

Notes on video

⮂ Discuss: 'After' church

1. At your church, what tends to happen in the time after the formal part of church is over? What's good and not so good?

2. Who do you normally talk to, and what do you talk about?

3. Do you find it difficult to talk about spiritual matters? If so, why is that, do you think?

4. If you do happen to talk to a newcomer, how do you find it?

 **Video: How to build over coffee**

Notes on video

🔁 Discuss: Speaking God's word to each other

1. Look up some (or all) of the following Bible verses. What do they teach about the 'everyday Word ministry' we can have to one another?

   * 1 Thessalonians 4:13-18

   * Hebrews 3:12-14

   * Colossians 3:14-17

   * Ephesians 4:11-16

2. Think about the sermon from last Sunday. What comment or question could you have used to begin a conversation centred on God's word?

3. What sorts of things stop us from ministering to others informally at church?

4. What does all this mean for what time we leave church?

 **Prayer**

Close in prayer together, giving thanks for the progress made so far, and asking for God's Spirit to help us keep going.

Assignment

Try to initiate at least one of the following this Sunday:
- a conversation about some specific point in the sermon
- praying with someone
- swapping stories of conversion with someone.

LOVING THE OUTSIDER

 **Discuss**

The practical exercise for this past week was to try to initiate:

- a conversation about some specific point in the sermon
- praying with someone
- swapping stories of conversion with someone.

How did it go? Pray together for any issues that arose out of your conversations.

 **Video: Is church just for Christians?**

Notes on video

● Discuss

1. Why do you think people are sometimes reluctant to bring friends or family with them to church?

2. What experiences have you had in bringing non-Christians to church?

3. Who in your group or in your church was converted through an invitation to church?

4. What stops you from inviting unbelievers to church?

5. What would you change about your church meeting and environment to make it more accessible and friendly for outsiders?

6. Who could you talk with about these changes in a helpful way (without grumbling and complaining)?

7. Read Colossians 4:3-6. What are some wise ways of inviting people to church?

 **Video: Why we don't**

Notes on video

 **Prayer**

- Give thanks to God for his great love in reaching out to us and saving us through his Son. Pray for a heart like God's—that longs to see those around us saved.
- Pray for people you know who don't know Christ.

Assignment

Think of two or three people you could invite to church. Start praying and thinking about when and how you might invite them. Come to the next session ready to share your plans.

LOVING YOUR CHURCH

 **Discuss**

Share the names of people you'd like to invite to church, and how you plan to go about it. Pray for these people and for each other.

Review

See if you can complete these sentences as a way of revising what we've talked about so far in this course.

1. The best way to walk into church is...

2. We go to church *not* as _____ or _____

   but as _____ and _____.

3. The strongest and highest motive for all that we do at church is...

4. We gather together in church in order to...

5. Building the church is the job of...

6. I could prepare to build at church by...

7. I could build and encourage those around me during the meeting by...

8. I could encourage other people in the informal time by...

9. We should invite our non-Christian friends to church because...

 **Video: Obstacles to loving your church**

Notes on video

 **Discuss**

1. What will stop us serving from the pew?

2. As a result of this course, how will you think differently about church?

3. What have you learned or discovered in the assignments that you'd like to continue and develop?

4. How would the principles of this course apply to your attitude and approach to other aspects of life—for example, your Bible study group? Is it any different?

5. What do you plan to do differently as a result of this course?

 **Concluding video**

Notes on video

 **Prayer**

- Give thanks for specific things you have learned over the past six sessions, and for conversations and encouragement you have been able to give to others at church.
- Pray for people you have ministered to.
- Pray that God would help you to continue to have a servant's heart, and to grow in love for those around you at church.

Feedback on this resource

We really appreciate getting feedback about our resources—not just suggestions for how to improve them, but also positive feedback and ways they can be used. We especially love to hear that the resources may have helped someone in their Christian growth.

You can send feedback to us via the 'Feedback' menu in our online store, or write to us at info@matthiasmedia.com.au.

LEADER'S NOTES

What is *Six Steps To Loving Your Church*?

It is very common for Christians to regard church as a passive, personal or receptive experience—as being about 'what I get out of it'.

At its best, this attitude tends to focus on the quality of the personal worship experience I am having and the personal lessons and encouragement I am receiving. At its worst, it leads Christians to evaluate church on the basis of whether they find it entertaining, enjoyable or beneficial; to have minimal interaction or participation while they are there; and even to 'shop around' for the church that delivers them the best experience.

However, church by its very nature is not a personal experience. It's a corporate one. And according to the New Testament, the key attitude we should bring with us to church is *love*: that consistent desire and determination to build up (or 'edify') others and seek their welfare. On the basis of love, we should come to church more ready to serve and build than to be entertained or inspired.

Six Steps to Loving Your Church is a simple six-step training program that helps participants change their whole mindset about church—to learn that 'loving' your church doesn't just mean enjoying it or liking it, but *loving the people who are the church* by ministering to them in whatever way you can.

It aims to transform congregation members from passive recipients or spectators to active other-person-centred servants in our Sunday gatherings; it aims to transform your church culture from 'the ministry of the few' to 'the ministry of the pew'.

The course also provides simple practical steps and exercises to equip participants in this 'ministry of the pew'—before, during and after the main church Sunday gathering.

Six Steps to Loving Your Church is ideal for small home Bible study groups.

Leading a group through *Six Steps to Loving Your Church*

Each session of the course consists of a mix of:
- group discussion and brainstorming
- Bible study
- video input
- practical exercises to try at church on Sunday
- feedback the following week on how those exercises went
- prayer.

These leader's notes contain information and tips for the leader—both about each session as a whole, and about the individual components of the sessions.

Here are some general tips about how to make the most of the training material.

1. Before

Although the material is pretty straightforward, an hour or so of preparation in advance for each session will greatly enhance your leading. In the following notes you'll find:
- a summary of the goal of each session
- a guide as to the timing of each element so as to complete the session in under an hour
- space to plan your own timing for each session

- suggestions and answers, where appropriate, for various components of each session.

In preparing for each session, make sure you work through all the Bible study and discussion sections, jotting down your own answers and summaries, and make sure you also watch the video segments.

Check the timing that is suggested for the different components, and make any adjustments according to how much time you have available in the group.

Finally, make sure you have the arrangements in place to play the video segments simply and easily, whether by having a DVD queued up and ready to play, or by having another device ready to stream the video direct from the GoThereFor.com website.

2. During

Most of the principles that apply to running any Bible study or training group are relevant for running the sessions of this course. Three in particular are worth noting:

- Let the conversation and discussion run freely; don't clamp down on people too quickly. It's important that participants have a chance not only to express their current feelings and attitudes towards church, but also to discuss and debate the ideas presented in the course, and work their way through them. For many people, the ideas in this course will be challenging. Give them time and space to work it through.
- At the same time, keep things on track. In particular, because we are discussing 'church', be careful not to allow the discussion to descend into a session about all that is wrong with church, or to get sidetracked into an opinion-fest about the kind of music we should be having, and so on. Stick to the core issue—which is how we think about church, and the attitude we take with us to church on Sunday. Don't let the various shortcomings of your church (and all churches have them!) distract participants from the need to change their own attitude and approach to church.

- Because *Six Steps to Loving Your Church* is a practical training program that aims to change not only minds but actions, it is vital that you lead the group not only by guiding them through the ideas but by putting the ideas into practice yourself. It's very important that you (as the leader) set an example—of admitting your own failings in loving people at church, and of seeking to do the practical exercises that are contained in each session.

[As a small practical point: in the busyness of life, you may find that participants get to church on Sunday and simply forget to do the practical exercises. A reminder email or text message on Saturday afternoon or Sunday morning might be useful.]

3. After

You might think through how you want to consolidate and continue the gains made through the course in the weeks and months following. Try making your 'ministry of the pew' on Sundays a regular ongoing discussion and prayer point of the group—for example, by praying for people you spoke to or encouraged on the previous Sunday.

Goal of the session

This opening session aims to draw out current attitudes towards church, and what we think church is about. It paints a contrast between the common thoughts and feelings people have as they walk into church and a different approach: what would it be like if we walked into church *praying about where to sit?* This would indicate that we saw church as a place where God had a ministry for us; where we expected to help and encourage others, and where we asked God to direct us to the people he wanted us to love.

Outline of the session with timing

Activity	Suggested timing	Your timing
Getting started	10 min	
Video: How do you walk into church?	4 min	4 min
Discuss: Your church	15 min	
Video: What is God thinking?	3 min	3 min
Discuss: A different walk	15 min	
Prayer	5 min	
Assignment (briefly discuss)	5 min	

Getting started

If your group is new or has gathered especially to do this course, take a few minutes to get to know each other. Then read through the course introduction together. Explain to the group that:

- the goal is to rethink what church is really about, and to re-examine our attitudes and behaviour as we go there
- the first two weeks of the course will focus on our beliefs and attitudes towards church, and the following weeks on what this means in practice
- throughout the course there will be a mix of discussion, Bible study and video input, as well as week-to-week exercises to help in beginning to put the ideas into practice

Lead the group in prayer for the weeks to come: that God would change your minds, hearts and actions by his Spirit.

Video: How do you walk into church?

In this (and subsequent) video sections, encourage the group to jot brief notes in the space provided as they listen.

Discuss: Your church

Much of the discussion in this section is to unearth how the group members are currently thinking and feeling about church. For questions 1-5, don't look for 'right' answers or get into too much debate—the aim is to get existing ideas out into the open and exposed to the light of day.

Be careful under question 3 that it doesn't descend into a complaint session. The aim of this question is for the group to name the fact that church is not always enjoyable or entertaining—that often church can be confronting, humdrum, of poor quality or irritating (either because of church or because of us and how we happen to be feeling).

Some key points for question 6:

- In Christ, God loved the church and gave himself up for her—to wash and sanctify her.
- God's purpose for the church is that she be splendid, holy, blameless, pure.
- God dwells in the church by his Spirit, and so it is his temple (not the church building but the congregation!).
- The church is therefore holy and precious to God—which means we must be very careful how we 'build'. To damage, let alone destroy, God's church is a terrible crime.

Discuss: A different walk

The purpose of this discussion is to begin to lift the participants' eyes from their own likes and dislikes at church to what church is really about—in particular to the key mind-shift of this course: that church is about other people; about opening our eyes and looking around us, and noticing all the people there just waiting to be encouraged and ministered to.

Assignment

The assignments are a key part of the content of the course. Impress upon the group that change comes not only through thinking new or clearer thoughts, but also through putting them into practice.

The normal pattern will be that each session concludes with a practical exercise or two to do at church the following Sunday; and that the following session starts with everyone giving some feedback on how the exercise went, what they learned, and so on. Let the group know that you will be talking about each assignment and how it went at the beginning of the following session.

If possible, send an email or text message to the group on Saturday or Sunday morning to remind them about the assignment.

SESSION 2: BUILDING IN LOVE

Goal of the session

This session lays down the biblical foundations for seeing church as a place where we love and edify one another, via a study of 1 Corinthians 13-14 and Hebrews 10. This is the critical change in mindset that this course is built on—moving from a view of church that is centred largely on ourselves (even on our own personal 'worship experience') to an understanding that is centred on God and those around us; to see church as a place where we love people by seeking to build them up in Christ.

Outline of the session with timing

Activity	Suggested timing	Your timing
Discuss	9 min	
Video: Building or spectating?	3 min	3 min
Bible study: Building in love	20 min	
Video: What church is about	6 min	6 min
Discuss: Are you a builder?	12 min	
Prayer	5 min	
Assignment (briefly discuss)	3 min	

Discuss

Talk through how the assignment went last Sunday. Encourage everyone about the importance of the practical assignments for getting the most out of the course (you get out what you put in).

Bible study: Building in love

This is not an easy Bible study, for a couple of reasons.

Firstly, although we look at two key New Testament passages about church, there is not the time and space to develop a comprehensive theology of church, nor to deal with many of the issues that have divided Christians on the subject over the centuries—such as the most appropriate models of church membership and leadership, or the most desirable styles of 'worship'. The study doesn't venture into these subjects, nor in a sense should it. The key idea to explore is the one that looms largest in the New Testament passages on church: the edification principle—that what happens in the congregational gathering should be driven and regulated by a loving desire to build others up in the Lord.

As mentioned above, this is the critical change in mindset that the course aims to achieve—moving people on from a view of church that is centred largely on ourselves to an understanding that is centred on God and those around us; to see church as a place where we love our brothers and sisters by seeking to build them up in Christ. Hopefully, by focusing on this important principle, Bible-believing churches with different views about structure and church government can all benefit.

Secondly, the study is a little tricky because of the controversial nature of some of the subject matter in 1 Corinthians 14. Fortunately the main point of the passage is very clear even if some of the details are a little harder to nail down (such as precisely what Paul means by 'prophecy' and 'tongues')—namely, that the thing to really pursue and practise in church is intelligible speech that builds up others.

Question 2: Love is the supreme principle that enables us to use our various gifts and contributions for the common good. Love focuses patiently and kindly on the other; it wants the truth to be spoken. It is more interested in seeing others grow in the Lord than in me expressing myself or being entertained or satisfied.

Question 4: The key factor is intelligibility. Prophecy is an encouraging, edifying word from God that is clear and understandable to others (as opposed to 'tongues', which is foreign to the hearer unless interpreted).

Question 5: By the principle of love, we should pursue intelligible encouraging speech such as prophecy or the various kinds of speech mentioned in 14:26, because they are for the good of others.

Question 6: Paul wants them to earnestly desire gifts, especially prophecy (v. 1); he is keen for them all to prophesy (v. 5); and he envisages them all coming to the gathering with some sort of word to share (v. 26). So the edifying speech is by no means limited just to the pastors or elders. All have a part to play. However, this doesn't mean chaos. There is order and peace—not everyone trying to speak at once.

Question 7: We gain access through the new and living way; through the blood of Jesus.

Question 8: Our access to God through faith in Christ gives us a certain hope for the last day; a hope of salvation. But in the meantime, we hold fast to that hope in the midst of a sinful and evil world. This is one of the key themes of Hebrews: the need to persevere, to stand firm, to not neglect or drift away from the great salvation that Jesus has brought. Here that need to "hold fast the confession of our hope without wavering" is supported by the role we have to encourage and help one another. As we persevere and wait for that day, we are to meet together for mutual encouragement and to stir one another up to love and good works.

Discuss: Are you a builder?

Question 1: Many people may have put something like 'to worship God' in their one-sentence explanation. Without getting into an argument about the nature of 'worship', it's worth pointing out that while church is certainly somewhere that we worship God (as we do throughout our lives), on its own 'worship' is not an adequate description of what church is about and why we go there. If our explanation doesn't include something about loving and serving our brothers and sisters by building them up in Christ, then we haven't understood what the Bible says about church.

Question 2: Symptoms might include getting in and out quickly; assessing church on the basis of whether it satisfies me; wanting high-quality service at minimum cost; having a critical spirit; blaming the management; attending as needed for spiritual therapy; having little or no relationship with others; going church shopping when I'm dissatisfied.

Question 3: Fruits would include expecting that God will speak to us; praying that God will hear us; being eager to meet with the family; being sad when a family member is absent; being observant of others' needs; being hospitable towards new people; coming early and staying late; and so on.

Question 4: It's very possible to enjoy church and be blessed by going there, but actually to do very little to love our brothers and sisters. This is the little play on words in the title of this course: it's not really about how much we 'love' (i.e. like) our church; it's about how much we love others in our service of them at church.

Question 5: A servant heart is the character of discipleship—laying down our lives in love for others, as Christ did on the cross. This attitude will transform our church-going.

Assignment

Briefly explain the exercise for this week, and then close the session by praying about what you've learned together. Pray that God would enlarge your hearts to love one another at church.

Goal of the session

If our goal is to build up and encourage one another at church, how might we *prepare* to do this before we even get to church? We could read the passage for the day in advance, pray for the meeting, and come early and ready to serve others.

How could we love and encourage our brothers and sisters *during* the meeting? In many ways: by our hearty singing, by speaking informally as we have opportunity, by active listening to the sermon, by looking for newcomers and visitors, and so on.

This session gets down to the practical suggestions for how we can be builders and encouragers on Sunday mornings.

Outline of the session with timing

Activity	Suggested timing	Your timing
Discuss	10 min	
Video: Preparing to build	1½ min	1½ min
Discuss: Be prepared	12 min	
Video: How to build *during* the meeting	5½ min	5½ min
Discuss: Better building	17 min	
Prayer	6 min	
Assignment (briefly discuss)	4 min	

Discuss: Be prepared

This is a fairly free-flowing brainstorm. As you draw the threads together, you might like to make sure that these sorts of points have emerged:

- Pray: for the preacher and all upfront people, for those who are to attend, for where I should sit, and for opportunities.
- Read the sermon passage: this not only helps us enormously, and is not only an encouragement to the preacher, but it also equips us to discuss and talk with others.
- Be ready to meet new people: look out for them, welcome them (whether on their own or as guests of others), sit with them.
- Organize yourself to arrive early with expectations to meet new people, welcome new people, and so on.

Discuss: Better building

Again, the idea here is for people to see that once you have the mindset of service and building, there is a multitude of ways to put it into practice.

SESSION 4: LOVE OVER COFFEE

Goal of the session

This session focuses on the informal time that follows most church meetings, where we continue our fellowship over refreshments. This is a key time for 'the ministry of the pew'—for taking opportunities to talk together about the content of the sermon, share stories of how God has worked in our lives, pray for one another, and so on.

Outline of the session with timing

Activity	Suggested timing	Your timing
Discuss	8 min	
Video: When does church finish?	2 min	2 min
Discuss: 'After' church	15 min	
Video: How to build over coffee	12 min	12 min
Discuss: Speaking God's word to each other	15 min	
Prayer	4 min	
Assignment (briefly discuss)	3 min	

Discuss: 'After' church

The aim of this discussion is to draw out some honest reflections on how our 'coffee time' conversations often go. Don't try to come up with all the answers at this point.

It is possible that the video input on 'When does church finish?' might prompt some theological debate about the nature of church, the marks of the church, and so on. Even if you (or your group) don't agree with the idea that the 'after church' time could still be defined as 'church', use this disagreement to draw out the important issue—that the time 'after church' is a vital opportunity for mutual encouragement and ministry.

Discuss: Speaking God's word to each other

In order to reinforce the really important theological point from the video—namely that the engine of mutual encouragement is the speaking of God's word to each other—the discussion starts with some relevant verses on this topic. Read and discuss as many of these as you have time for.

Question 1: All these passages emphasize the reality of Christians exhorting and encouraging each other. (1 Thessalonians 4:18 and Colossians 3:16 were mentioned in the video.) Hebrews 3:12-14 doesn't specifically mention using God's word in our exhortation, but in the context of the whole passage (which is about our hearing of and obedience to God's word) the content of the exhortation is to continue in faith and obedience to God's word. Ephesians 4:11-16 is a slightly tricky passage, especially working out precisely what verses 11-12 are referring to. However, the overall point is clear enough—that the church "builds itself up in love" as we all speak the true doctrine of Christ to one another.

Question 3: Things like leaving as soon as possible; personal lack of confidence or shyness; fear that others will think of us as superior or 'super-spiritual'; embarrassment; lack of thought and preparation; and so on.

Question 4: It means we stay late, and if possible take someone home with us for lunch (or supper)!

SESSION 5: LOVING THE OUTSIDER

Goal of the session

How does our attitude of love and service extend to the outsider—to our friends and family who don't come to church? This session talks about inviting our non-Christian friends and family to church, and the issues that this raises—about our own fears and reluctance to issue the invitation, and about how welcoming and intelligible our church meetings are for the outsider.

Outline of the session with timing

Activity	Suggested timing	Your timing
Discuss	10 min	
Video: Is church just for Christians?	4½ min	4½ min
Discuss	23 min	
Video: Why we don't (interview)	10 min	10 min
Prayer	8 min	
Assignment (briefly discuss)	4 min	

Discuss

There are two possibly difficult issues to navigate in this discussion. The first is that your group members may not have thought about church as a place for inviting non-Christians, and may feel awkward or uncomfortable about it. Talk about this honestly—how much of our discomfort is 'fear of man' or lack of concern for people's salvation? It's worth pointing out that people are often far more willing to come to church than we are to invite them!

However, the second and trickier problem is that your church might not currently be the sort of place where the 1 Corinthians 14 experience is likely to happen—that is, where non-Christians are likely to hear God's word clearly and intelligibly. If that's the case, your group might not be in much of a position to change this—in the short term, at least. Questions 5 and 6 cover this issue in a way that is designed to be constructive (i.e. avoiding complaining or negativity).

Question 7: It's often helpful to invite people not to church in general (it sounds like they have to join) but to a specific meeting. Invite them to hear a particular preacher or topic, or to a new sermon series or a guest service.

Assignment

The idea is to get people thinking and praying and getting used to the idea of inviting someone to church. At the beginning of the final session, you'll share the names of the people you'd like to invite, and pray for God's help in the process.

Goal of the session

This concluding session summarizes and consolidates the ideas covered over the previous five sessions. In particular, this session reinforces that what we've been learning together is not just a few tips or techniques, but a way of life. It's a new orientation focused on other people rather than ourselves, where we try to do whatever we can to build and encourage others in order to see them saved and grow to maturity in Christ.

This session also deals with common obstacles to 'the ministry of the pew', as well as discussing how we can continue to grow and develop in this area after the training course has concluded.

It is therefore particularly important that you consider how you are going to follow on from this course. How are the members of your group going to keep embedding and practising 'the ministry of pew' within their lives? If you are using this program as part of an ongoing small group (and this a good reason for doing so), then make discussion and prayer about these issues a regular ongoing part of your group life together.

Outline of the session with timing

Activity	Suggested timing	Your timing
Discuss	8 min	
Review	7 min	
Video: Obstacles to loving your church (interview)	10 min	10 min
Discuss	20 min	
Concluding video	3 min	3 min
Prayer	10 min	

Discuss/review

1. The best way to walk into church is… to pray about where you sit.

2. We go to church NOT as consumers or spectators but as loving servants and builders.

3. The strongest and highest motive for all that we do at church is... to love; to seek the growth of others.

4. We gather together in church in order to... build and encourage one another in God's presence through the prayerful speaking of God's word to each other.

5. Building the church is the job of... all the members of the body.

6. I could prepare to build at church by... reading the passage beforehand, praying, considering, planning to be there early.

7. I could build and encourage those around me during the meeting by... everything I do: singing, active listening, speaking as I have opportunity, and so on.

8. I could encourage other people in the informal time by... talking about God's word from the sermon; praying; sharing stories of grace; looking out for newcomers.

9. We should invite our non-Christian friends to church because... it's a great place for them to hear God's word in the context of Christian friendship.

Video: Obstacles to loving your church (interview)

The aim of the interview with Colin (and the subsequent discussion) is twofold:
- to bring out into the open any lingering questions or impediments about the every-member pew ministry this course has been advocating
- to encourage each participant to articulate what they have learned and to resolve to continue putting these new insights and skills into practice.

Prayer

Before you pray together, it would be worth talking about what you as a group could do to continue the momentum you've built up. Have a regular report or prayer time about your ministry each Sunday (who you talked to, what you could pray for them, and so on); work together to invite non-Christian friends to a particular church meeting in the future; and so on.

Then conclude in prayer together that God would help you to put it all into practice.

HOW TO USE THIS COURSE IN YOUR CHURCH

(FOR PASTORS AND CHURCH LEADERS)

Changing the culture

Over the past few years, in the aftermath of *The Trellis and the Vine*, Col Marshall and I have run numerous workshops around the world on how to spread a 'vine-oriented' culture in our churches. We've talked with many pastors about how we can make sure that our churches don't become dominated by structures and programs, but have a strong heartbeat of 'people ministry'—of each congregation member seeking to be a disciple-maker in their own way.

Spreading this kind of culture in a church is not a simple or one-off activity. It's a process (often painful) that takes time and persistence. However, one easy, straightforward way of beginning to change the mindset and culture of our church members is to change the way they think about Sunday. That's what this training program is really about.

It aims to do two things:

- It aims to change people's minds about our Sunday church gatherings—away from seeing church as being just an event or structure that I attend for my own personal benefit or interaction with God, and towards seeing church as a God-given opportunity to love and encourage and minister to other people; from being merely a recipient and consumer to being an active participant and encourager.

- It aims to give some simple, easy-to-implement steps for starting to do this Sunday by Sunday.

As a way of changing your church culture, *Six Steps to Loving Your Church* is an easy first step. It's an enjoyable and non-threatening course that enables participants to take small and achievable steps towards ministering to others (that is, to start to become a 'disciple-making disciple').

You might consider combining the course with a sermon series on 'church'—on what the Bible teaches about the nature and purposes of church in God's plans. The course does not attempt to articulate a complete theology of church—not only because this is beyond its scope, but also because within Bible-teaching evangelical churches there are some obvious differences around this issue. We have consciously designed the material in the course to focus in on the issue of how all congregation members can love and encourage and minister to one another on Sundays, without venturing into questions of church structure or government, or music and service styles, or other similar issues. This is not to say that these questions are unimportant—only that regardless of our stance on these sorts of questions, equipping our members to be loving servants and encouragers on Sunday would be a significant step forward.

Existing small groups or one-off training?

Like other courses in the *Six Steps* series, *Six Steps to Loving Your Church* is designed as practical, easy-to-run training for small home Bible study groups (or whatever you call them in your part of the world):

- The Bible study and discussion questions are not complicated or difficult, and answer guides are provided for leaders.
- The video input segments supply key content, as well as summarizing and tying together the sessions.
- There are practical exercises for the group members to do each

week in church, which they then talk about the following week in the group (and having this conversation as part of an existing group that already knows each other is helpful).

- Six sessions is a good number to do in a regular small group— it's enough to make a difference and see real progress in understanding and action, but without interrupting the normal (and proper) diet of regular Bible study.
- The course teaches a change in mindset that is expressed in practical ways—and this doesn't stop after six weeks! By running the course in an existing (and ongoing) small group, the gains made over the six sessions can be consolidated and worked on over the ensuing weeks and months.

So although you could usefully set up a group or structure specifically for running this training—as part of an existing ministry training structure, or as a special training emphasis—the ideal and obvious way to use *Six Steps to Loving Your Church* is to roll it out through existing small group structures.

If you set up a special training structure for utilizing the course, you will need to think through how to follow through on the ideas and actions *after* the six sessions are concluded—because a change of mindset and behaviour takes time, and we easily slip back into old habits. Perhaps the training group could decide to reconvene every three months during the following year to talk about how their 'ministry of the pew' is going, to pray for one another, and to share ideas.

Leader training

If you were going to roll out the training material through existing small groups, it would be very beneficial to conduct some brief orientation and training for your small group leaders. This could be part of your regular meetings with small group leaders (assuming you have such meetings), or a one-off evening where you introduce the course and equip the leaders with some basic information about why you are using this course and how to run it.

A training evening could have the following content.

A. Start with this brief Bible study (based on session 2 of the course).

---

1. If you had just one sentence to explain why you go to church, what would you say?

2. Read 1 Corinthians 13:1-7. The famous chapter on love is part of Paul's teaching on using one's gifts in church. Why do you think he describes love as the "more excellent way" (1 Cor 12:31)?

   Love is the supreme principle that enables us to use our various gifts and contributions for the common good. Love focuses patiently and kindly on the other; it wants the truth to be spoken. It is more interested in seeing others grow in the Lord than in me expressing myself or being entertained or satisfied.

3. Read 1 Corinthians 14:1-12, 26-33.
   a. What is it about prophecy that makes it better than speaking in tongues in church?

   The key factor is intelligibility. Prophecy is an encouraging, edifying word from God that is clear and understandable to others (as opposed to 'tongues', which is foreign to the hearer unless interpreted).

---

b. How do you think this relates to love in chapter 13?

By the principle of love, we should pursue intelligible encouraging speech such as prophecy or the various kinds of speech mentioned in 14:26, because they are for the good of others.

4. How well do you think our congregation grasps this basic idea and puts it into practice on Sundays?

B. Watch the introductory *Six Steps to Loving Your Church* video (or give your own short talk based on the video and on the information provided at the beginning of appendix 1).

C. Explain why small home groups are an ideal way to do this training (using the points outlined above).

D. Direct the leaders to the leader's notes in appendix 1, which give practical guidance on running the sessions. In particular, at the start of each session you'll find some information on the goal of that session. Suggest that the leaders read these now so they get a sense of the whole course.

E. Field questions about all of the above.

F. Pray together

Matthias Media is an evangelical publishing ministry that seeks to persuade all Christians of the truth of God's purposes in Jesus Christ as revealed in the Bible, and equip them with high-quality resources, so that by the work of the Holy Spirit they will:

- abandon their lives to the honour and service of Christ in daily holiness and decision-making
- pray constantly in Christ's name for the fruitfulness and growth of his gospel
- speak the Bible's life-changing word whenever and however they can—in the home, in the world and in the fellowship of his people.

Our resources range from Bible studies and books through to training courses, audio sermons and children's Sunday School material. To find out about more, and to access samples and free downloads, visit our website:

www.matthiasmedia.com

How to buy our resources

1. Direct from us over the internet:
   – in the US: www.matthiasmedia.com
   – in Australia: www.matthiasmedia.com.au

2. Direct from us by phone:
   – in the US: 1 866 407 4530
   – in Australia: 1300 051 220
   – international: +61 2 9233 4627

> Register at our website for our **free** regular email update to receive information about the latest new resources, **exclusive special offers,** and free articles to help you grow in your Christian life and ministry.

3. Through a range of outlets in various parts of the world. Visit **www.matthiasmedia.com/contact** for details about recommended retailers in your part of the world, including www.thegoodbook.co.uk in the United Kingdom.

4. Trade enquiries can be addressed to:
   – in the US and Canada: sales@matthiasmedia.com
   – in Australia and the rest of the world: sales@matthiasmedia.com.au

5. Visit **GoThereFor.com** for subscription-based access to a great-value range of digital resources.